C000203737

£4.50

CONTENTS

Published by World International Publishing Limited, An Egmont Company,
P.O. Box 111, Great Ducie Street, Manchester M60 3BL. Printed in Great Britain.
Copyright © DC Comics Inc. 1991. All rights reserved. The stories, characters
and names featured in this publication are the property of DC Comics Inc.
and are used under licence from DC Comics Inc. Any inquiries should be
addressed to DC Comics Inc., c/o London Editions Magazines.

ISBN 0 7498 0404 1

As abruptly as it began, the paper storm ends...and...

Another *victim!* This one looks like he's been *crushed* to death...as if by a *boa constrictor!* Charming!

The killer's *method* may vary from murder to murder...

...but his *calling card* remains the same, a chain of *paper dolls* draped across the *victim's torso!* Talk about *sick...*

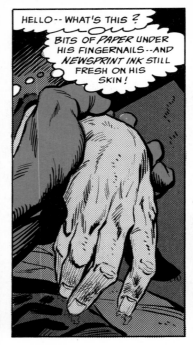

Hello-- what's this *?* Bits of *paper* under his *fingernails* --and *newsprint ink* still fresh on his *skin!*

Ten victims in *three* weeks-- ranging from *junkies* and *derelicts* to a few *college kids* who'd had a bit too much to *drink!*

What in *heaven's name* is the *connection?*

And, as the Batman ponders that...

...nearby, at the studios of *wham-tv...*

For the *third* week, Gotham is *terrorized* by these grisly so-called "*doll murders*"...

...the latest *symptom* of America's moral *decay!*

Moral laxity in the *media*...the assault on the *family unit* in the name of "*equal rights*"...

Too long have a handful of *freaks* and *malcontents* subverted the *traditional* values the *majority* of Americans *cherish--!*

Commentary WITH DR. CLAYTON WHITLEY Ph.D.

WHAM TV

WATCHING FROM THE *DIRECTOR'S BOOTH*, WHAM'S ACE TROUBLE-SHOOTER, *JACK RYDER*, AND STATION MANAGER *HUGO MARLIES*...

HUGO, THE MAN'S A *REACTIONARY LOON!* AND YOU GIVE HIM HIS OWN SHOW?

LOTSA PEOPLE WANT TO *HEAR* WHAT HE HAS TO SAY, JACK! BESIDES...

...THAT COULD'VE BEEN *YOUR* SHOW! YOU'RE THE ONE WHO GAVE UP NEWSCASTING TO WORK IN SECURITY, REMEMBER?

I HAD MY *REASONS*, HUGO...

YEAH--LIKE THINKING I'D HAVE MORE FREEDOM TO BECOME THE *CREEPER* WHEN NECESSARY...

STILL, WETLEY *BURNS* ME! HE OFFERS NO *SOLUTIONS*-- ONLY ANGER! I WISH I COULD--

ONE SIDE, RYDER! MAKE WAY FOR THE *PRESS!*

VERA! HOW'S OUR RESIDENT *NEWS VULTURE?* SEEN ANY GOOD *MUTILATING ACCIDENTS* LATELY?

VERY FUNNY, HOTSHOT! I GOTTA FIND A *MINICAM UNIT*, QUICK-- THIS JUST CAME IN OVER THE WIRE--

STUDIO 3

--THAT *PAPER DOLL TWISTO* JUST *ACED* SOMEBODY ELSE ON *TEMPLE STREET!*

IF I'M LUCKY I CAN HAVE THE CORPSE ON THE AIR BY *ELEVEN*...

GOOD OLD *VERA!* MY OWN PRIVATE *GAZETTE*--WITH *FANGS!* DON'T *TURN*, HONEY...

...NOT THAT YOU'D TRY TO *STOP* ME, OF COURSE...

ACTIVATING THE MOLECULAR *TRANSMUTER* BENEATH HIS SKIN, *JACK RYDER* IS INSTANTLY TRANSFORMED INTO--

7

...**THE CREEPER!**
WANTED BY THE POLICE -- WANTED
BY THE UNDERWORLD --

TEMPLE STREET ISN'T *FAR*...

...SHOULD MAKE IT THERE INSIDE OF FIVE --

LOOK! UP THERE! IT'S THE *CREEPER!*

HE'S A *FREAK* -- JUST LIKE THAT *DOLL KILLER!*

WETLEY IS RIGHT -- THEY'RE ALL *ALIKE!* WE GOTTA GET *THEM* BEFORE THEY GET *US!*

GET HIM! GET THE LOUSY *FREAK!*

OH, *GREAT!* *THIS* I NEEDED?

ARROGANT HUMANS! I SHOULD DISPATCH YOU ALL TO THE *OBLIVION* RESERVED FOR *BIGOTS* AND *COWARDS* --

BUT I SHALL BE *MERCIFUL,* AND TAKE MY *LEAVE!*

HA HA HA HA HA

HA HA

WETLEY'S LITTLE *CHEERING* SECTION GETS NASTIER EVERY *DAY!* THEY'RE SCARED -- OF THE *KILLER,* OF A WORLD THEY DON'T *UNDERSTAND* ANYMORE --

-- BUT IS THAT ANY EXCUSE FOR *UNREASONING* HATE?

8

SKID ROW, 10:25 P.M.--

THE *FIRST* VICTIM WAS *BURNED* TO DEATH-- THE SECOND WAS *HUNG*, BUT WITH NO NOOSE IN EVIDENCE AND ONLY *PAPER BURNS* ON HIS NECK...

PRETTY *GRISLY*, EVEN FOR--

NO! STAY AWAY, MAN! STAY AWAY!!

POLLUTANT! YOUR KIND MUST BE *ELIMINATED*--!

MAMA!

WELL, WELL! *RENALDO!* I'VE BEEN *LOOKING* FOR YOU!

UH, ON *SECOND* THOUGHT, MAYBE I'LL TAKE MY CHANCES WITH THE *PSYCHO* HERE, OKAY?

HEY! *BATS!* LONG TIME NO SEE!

CREEPER?!

HA HA HA HA HA SO, VILE *MORTAL*-- PREPARE TO MEET YOUR--

HOLY--! DID I SAY *"MORTAL"?*

MY *GOD!* IT'S MADE OF-- *PAPER!* IT'S... SOME KIND OF MONSTER--!

HE CALLED YOU... *CREEPER*--?

9

CRIMINAL SCUM!

WE MUST CLEANSE OURSELVES...

...OF SUCH AS YOU!

UNNHHH!

PAPERS... SUDDENLY HARD AS STEEL! CONSTRICTING... SQUEEZING THE LIFE OUT OF ME--!

BATMAN!

HANG ON, CREEPER!

NO...YOU MUSTN'T! HE IS A POLLUTANT!

ARGHHH!!

THAT WASTE PAPER... THE CREATURE'S TURNED IT INTO MINIATURE MISSILES!

HITTING ME...LIKE STRAW PROPELLED BY A HURRICANE...

YOU ARE NO BETTER THAN *HE*... YOU, TOO, MUST *DIE*...

CREEPER CAN'T *LAST* MUCH LONGER... IF THIS *THING* REALLY IS A... A *PAPER MAN*, THEN I ONLY PRAY HE CAN ALSO --

--*BURN*!

ARGHHH

GOOD LORD-- HIS *HAND*! HE'S ...*NOT HUMAN*...

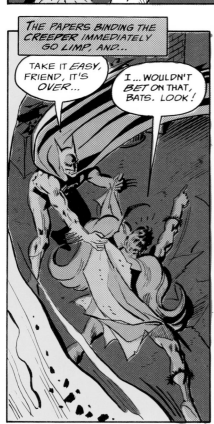

THE PAPERS BINDING THE *CREEPER* IMMEDIATELY GO LIMP, AND...

TAKE IT *EASY*, FRIEND, IT'S *OVER*...

I ... *WOULDN'T BET* ON THAT, BATS. LOOK!

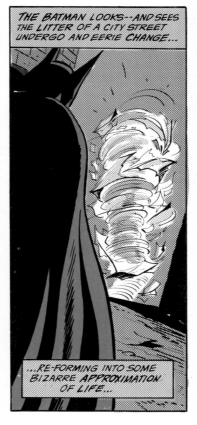

THE *BATMAN* LOOKS-- AND SEES THE *LITTER* OF A CITY STREET UNDERGO AND EERIE *CHANGE*...

...*RE-FORMING* INTO SOME *BIZARRE APPROXIMATION* OF LIFE...

AND, WITH A *SINGLE*, BACKWARD GLANCE, CHOOSING TO *RUN*...

...SO THAT IT MIGHT *KILL ANOTHER DAY*...

11

SHORTLY... IN THE BATCAVE...

WOW! SOME *PLACE* YOU GOT HERE, BATS! EVER THOUGHT OF GOING *CONDO*?

JACK? DO ME A *FAVOR*?

DON'T CALL ME *"BATS"*!

OH! SURE, B.M.!

MY *SPECTROANALYSIS* SHOWS THAT THIS PAPER THAT ALMOST *CRUSHED* YOU IS JUST THAT-- *PAPER*! SOMEHOW THAT *CREATURE* INCREASED ITS TENSILE STRENGTH *TENFOLD*!

ORDINARILY, I PREFER *RATIONAL* EXPLANATIONS...

...BUT THE EVIDENCE SUGGESTS WE'RE DEALING WITH SOMETHING *PARANORMAL*! TRYING TO DISCERN ITS *MOTIVES* WOULD PROBABLY BE FUTILE...

...SO WE'LL CONCENTRATE ON ITS *METHOD* OF OPERATION! LIKE ANOTHER SUPERNATURAL ENTITY-- *THE SPECTRE*-- ITS TARGETS SEEM TO BE CRIMINALS...

...SO I'LL PLOT A *GRAPH* OF THE HIGH-CRIME NEIGHBORHOODS, AND WE CAN STAKE THEM OUT TOMORROW NIGHT!

SOUNDS GOOD! AS FOR ME...

...I NEARLY GOT KILLED *TWICE* TONIGHT, ONCE BY OUR *KILLER PULPY*, ONCE BY AN *ANGRY MOB*!

SOMEBODY BETTER TALK SOME SENSE INTO *DR. WETLEY* BEFORE HIS TIRADES TOUCH OFF A *RIOT*!

GETTING *LATE*, B.M.! GIVE A FELLA A LIFT *HOME*?

CREEPER?

YEAH?

GO BACK TO *"BATS"*?

THE NEXT DAY...

RIOTS IN MIAMI... SENSELESS *MURDERS* HERE IN *GOTHAM*... THE TIME FOR ACTION IS *NOW*, MY FRIENDS!

THE WILL OF THE *MAJORITY* MUST BE *HEARD!*

HE'S *RIGHT!* THIS IS A *DEMOCRACY*-- THAT'S *MAJORITY RULE*, RIGHT?

ALL THIS TALK ABOUT *EQUAL RIGHTS* -- WELL, HOW ABOUT SOME EQUAL RIGHTS FOR *ME?*

WE GOTTA *DO* SOMETHING! BUT *WHAT?!*

AND, IN WETLEY'S ELEGANT HOME...

YOU'RE *EXPLOITING* THESE MURDERS, WETLEY--USING THEM TO CREATE *FEAR*--

--AND PEOPLE WHO ARE *AFRAID* ARE MORE LIKELY TO LISTEN TO YOUR *POLITICS*, AREN'T THEY?

IS THAT *RIGHTEOUS ANGER*--OR *JEALOUSY* THAT *I* HAVE THE AUDIENCE YOU *GAVE UP?*

LEAVE THE *COMMENTARY* TO ME, MR. RYDER-- AND *I'LL* LEAVE THE *SECURITY* TO *YOU!* HM?

GOOD DAY, MR. RYDER!

LATER...

I SPENT YEARS BEFORE THE CAMERAS... *GOOD* YEARS! I LIKE TO THINK I MADE SOME SMALL *DIFFERENCE!*

THEN I STARTED PLAYING *SUPER-HERO*... AND SLOWLY JACK RYDER BECAME JUST A *FACE* FOR THE *CREEPER* TO *HIDE* BEHIND!

AFTER ALL, BEING A *SUPER-HERO*... THAT'S MORE IMPORTANT, ISN'T IT?

WELL, LAST NIGHT THE *CREEPER* COULDN'T DO A BLASTED THING AGAINST THAT *MONSTER*...

...BUT MAYBE JACK RYDER, NEWSCASTER, *COULD'VE* DONE SOMETHING ABOUT THE MONSTER WETLEY IS CREATING...

13

VAYA LA *POLICIA*, SEÑORA! AHORA!

CREEPER! THE *FIRE ESCAPE!*

GOTCHA, B.M.!

HEY--PULPY! YOUR MOTHER WAS A *LOOSE-LEAF BINDER!*

SNAP

THWACK

OOOPS!

SWIFTLY, THE BATMAN SNAPS UP THE MONSTER'S DECAPITATED HEAD, ONLY TO FIND--

FOOL! WE ARE MORE THAN THE SUM OF OUR PARTS!

OH...MY... GOD...

WHAM

THEIR SCREAMS ECHO THROUGH THE GHETTO STREET, FADING ONLY AS THE TWO HEROES FALL, DEATH-LIKE, TO THE GROUND...

THINKING ITS ASSAILANTS *DEAD*, THE CREATURE TURNS AND STALKS AWAY... BUT...

GOT...TO GET... BATARANG... BEFORE IT GETS AWAY...

...AND HOPE OUR *SUPERNATURAL* FRIEND...

SMK

...*DOESN'T* NOTICE!

SHORTLY...

OUR MONSTER IS MADE OF *WASHI*-- A HANDMADE *PULP* PAPER SOMETIMES USED IN MAKING *ORIGAMI*-- JAPANESE *PAPER SCULPTURES!*

AND ACCORDING TO *DR. WU*, AN *ART DEALER* I JUST CALLED...

...ONE OF THE STATE'S FOREMOST *COLLECTORS* OF *ORIGAMI* IS NONE OTHER THAN ...*DR. CLAYTON WETLEY!*

MY GOD! THAT CREATURE TALKING ABOUT THE *"MAJORITY"*-- IS WETLEY *USING* IT TO *ELIMINATE* THOSE PARTS OF SOCIETY HE FINDS -- *UNDESIRABLE?*

WHAT DO YOU THINK DR. WETLEY WOULD THINK OF A *MID-NIGHT* VISIT BY THE *BATMAN* AND THE *CREEPER?*

I THINK HE'D BE SCARED *SPITLESS!* HA HA HA HA HA HA

UH, JUST *PRACTICING,* BATS...

AND, SO, SHORTLY...

YOU'RE -- YOU'RE BOTH *CRAZY!* HOW *DARE* YOU SUGGEST I HAD ANYTHING TO DO WITH THESE GRUESOME *MURDERS?!*

DO NOT *DISSEMBLE,* MORTAL! ADMIT YOUR *GUILT*--AND I SHALL BE *LENIENT!*

YOU HAVE YOUR *NERVE!* YOU AND YOUR KIND ARE THE REASON THIS COUNTRY IS IN SUCH *TROUBLE!*

YOUR SO-CALLED *HEROICS* EN- COURAGE YOUNG PEOPLE TO BE-- *DIFFERENT!* WE NEED FEWER *HEROES* -- AND MORE *PRODUCTIVE* CITIZENS!

NOW GET *OUT* OF HERE -- BEFORE I CALL THE *POLICE!*

IT'S TOO *PAT!* WHY WOULD WETLEY USE AN *ORIGAMI* AS HIS INSTRUMENT WHEN HE'S *KNOWN* AS A *COLLECTOR* OF THEM?

I HAVE A *THEORY,* JACK...

...BUT TO *TEST* IT WE'VE GOT TO CREATE AN *IRRESISTIBLE* *TARGET* FOR THE ORIGAMI!

FUNNY YOU SHOULD *MENTION* THAT, B.M. I'VE GOT *JUST* THE GUY...

THE COSTUMED FIGURES *VANISH* INTO THE NIGHT... AND BEHIND THEM, THE *ORIGAMI MAN* LOOKS AFTER, AN *EVIL GLINT* IN ITS *PAPER EYES...*

TWO DAYS LATER...

I'D LIKE TO *CLOSE* MY FIRST DAY BACK ON THE AIR WITH A *COMMENTARY!*

WE HEAR A *LOT* LATELY ABOUT THE "*WILL* OF THE *MAJORITY*"... BUT A *DEMOCRACY* DOESN'T MEAN FREEDOM FOR THE *MAJORITY* OF PEOPLE...

WHAM TV

NIGHT WATCH

...BUT FOR *ALL* PEOPLE! DEMOCRACY ISN'T FORCING *YOUR* IDEA OF WHAT'S *RIGHT* ON *EVERYONE* -- IT'S HAVING THE *FREEDOM* TO PRACTICE YOUR *OWN* MORALITY --

-- AND THE *COURAGE* TO ALLOW OTHERS TO PRACTICE *THEIRS!*

FOR *WHAM-TV,* THIS IS *JACK RYDER* -- GOOD NIGHT...

THAT *TOAD!* HE'S DOING THIS JUST TO *SPITE* ME! I'LL -- I'LL --

-- I'LL *KILL* HIM! HE *KNEW* I WANTED THAT *JOB,* AND HE TALKED *MARLIES* INTO HIRING *HIM!*

ARGHHH!!

AND, MINUTES LATER...

NICE *BROADCAST,* JACK! BUT DON'T YOU WORRY TAKING *STANDS* LIKE THAT WILL ENDANGER YOUR *SECRET IDENTITY?*

SURE, IT'S A *RISK!* BUT Y'KNOW, *BATS...* IF I HAD TO LIVE IN CONSTANT *FEAR* OF EXPOSING MY *IDENTITY...*

...IF THE ONLY WAY I COULD SHOW ANY *COURAGE* WAS PUTTING ON A *COSTUME...*

...WHAT THE HECK KIND OF *HERO* WOULD I BE?

WISH ME *LUCK,* BATMAN... AND KEEP *CLOSE,* HUH?

TAKE A *GOOD LOOK,* DOCTOR! THAT MONSTER IS *YOUR* DOING!

WHAT?!

IT IS *TRUE,* MORTAL! YOUR *BROADCASTS* PROMOTE ANGER AND *FRUSTRATION!*

SMAK!

WHAK

IT IS THE *SOULS* OF YOUR *LISTENERS* THAT MAKE THIS LIFELESS SHELL *MURDER!*

YOU'RE THE *PSYCHIC FOCUS,* WETLEY! YOUR *SUBCONSCIOUS*-- WITH ITS *LATENT PSYCHIC ABILITIES*--CHOSE AN *ORIGAMI* AS ITS *WEAPON!*

WHOOMP!

NO! IT *CAN'T BE!* NOTHING LIKE THIS HAS HAPPENED...SINCE I WAS A *CHILD*--!

AND EVEN THEN IT WAS ONLY *VISIONS*... *DREAMS*... *VOICES* IN MY *HEAD*--!

WETLEY--*LISTEN!* YOU'RE THE *CONDUIT* FOR YOUR *LISTENERS'* HATRED! IT'S LIKE A *CIRCUIT*--AND ONLY *YOU* CAN BREAK IT! ONLY YOU CAN *STOP*--

UUNNGGG!!

SPEED LIMIT 25

BLANG

20

THEY ALL *LAUGHED* AT ME... MADE *FUN* OF ME! YOU KNOW WHAT IT'S LIKE... BEING *DIFFERENT?* BEING *HATED?*

I SPENT ALL MY LIFE TRYING TO *FIT IN*... MAINTAINING THE *STATUS QUO...*

NOW-- *DIE!*

WHAM

BUT I'M *NOT A MURDERER!* I'M *NOT!*

I'M *NOT!!*

EEEYAHHHHHH

FOR *MINUTES,* ALL THAT CAN BE *HEARD* IS THE *CRACKLE* OF FIRE, AND WETLEY'S *MUTED SOBS...* THEN...

IT *WORKED,* CREEPER! IT'S *OVER!*

IS IT?

WETLEY WAS ONLY THE *FOCUS!* THE *REAL MURDERERS...* ARE STILL *OUT* THERE!

ALL THEY NEED... IS ANOTHER *FOCUS!*

SOMEHOW, BATS... I DON'T THINK IT IS *OVER...*

ENZ

21

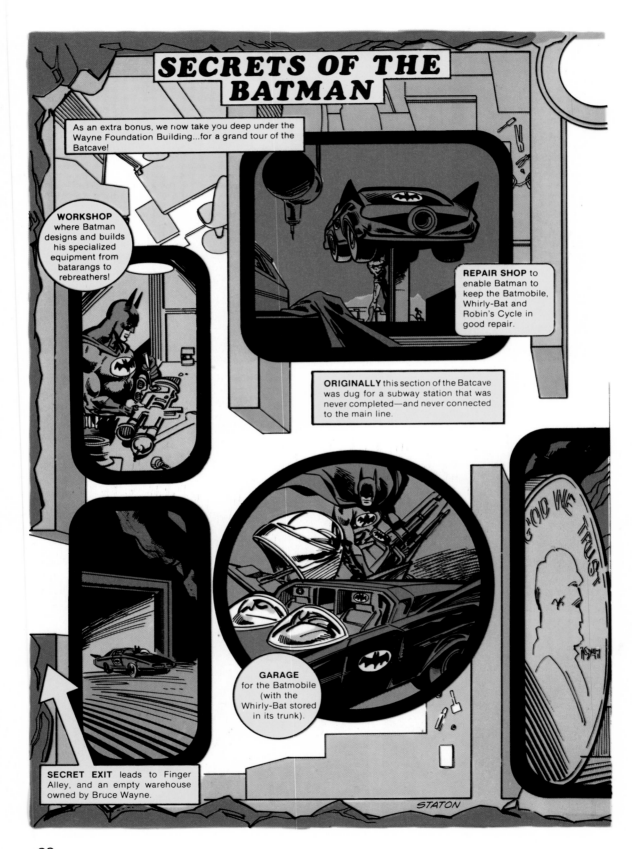

SECRETS OF THE BATMAN

As an extra bonus, we now take you deep under the Wayne Foundation Building...for a grand tour of the Batcave!

WORKSHOP where Batman designs and builds his specialized equipment from batarangs to rebreathers!

REPAIR SHOP to enable Batman to keep the Batmobile, Whirly-Bat and Robin's Cycle in good repair.

ORIGINALLY this section of the Batcave was dug for a subway station that was never completed—and never connected to the main line.

GARAGE for the Batmobile (with the Whirly-Bat stored in its trunk).

SECRET EXIT leads to Finger Alley, and an empty warehouse owned by Bruce Wayne.

STATON

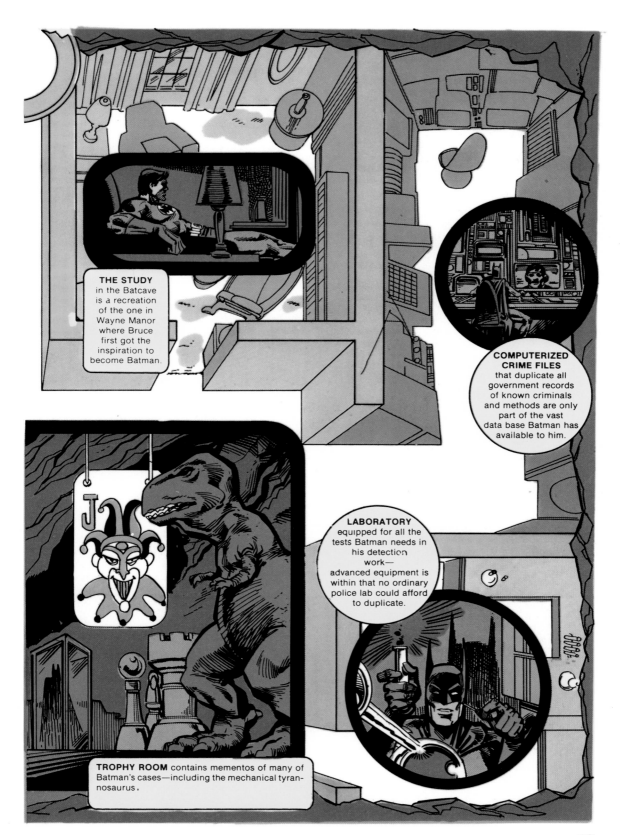

THE STUDY in the Batcave is a recreation of the one in Wayne Manor where Bruce first got the inspiration to become Batman.

COMPUTERIZED CRIME FILES that duplicate all government records of known criminals and methods are only part of the vast data base Batman has available to him.

LABORATORY equipped for all the tests Batman needs in his detection work— advanced equipment is within that no ordinary police lab could afford to duplicate.

TROPHY ROOM contains mementos of many of Batman's cases—including the mechanical tyrannosaurus.

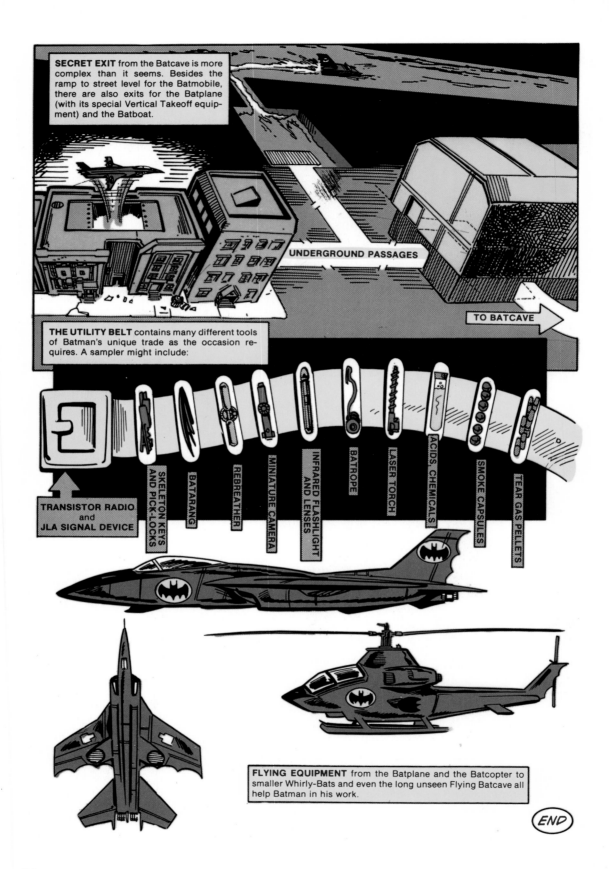

SECRET EXIT from the Batcave is more complex than it seems. Besides the ramp to street level for the Batmobile, there are also exits for the Batplane (with its special Vertical Takeoff equipment) and the Batboat.

UNDERGROUND PASSAGES

TO BATCAVE

THE UTILITY BELT contains many different tools of Batman's unique trade as the occasion requires. A sampler might include:

TRANSISTOR RADIO and JLA SIGNAL DEVICE

SKELETON KEYS AND PICK-LOCKS

BATARANG

REBREATHER

MINIATURE CAMERA

INFRARED FLASHLIGHT AND LENSES

BATROPE

LASER TORCH

ACIDS, CHEMICALS

SMOKE CAPSULES

TEAR GAS PELLETS

FLYING EQUIPMENT from the Batplane and the Batcopter to smaller Whirly-Bats and even the long unseen Flying Batcave all help Batman in his work.

END

BAT MAN and Robin THE TEEN WONDER T.M.

CREATED BY BOB KANE

YOU ARE WATCHING THE IMPOSSIBLE:

FOR NOT ONLY IS THE DREAD BATMAN BEING *BEATEN* BY A MERE GANGSTER... BUT THE GANGSTER IS *MATCHES MALONE*-- A COVER IDENTITY OF THE BATMAN HIMSELF!

EITHER THIS IS THE DARKNIGHT DETECTIVE'S MOST IGNOMINIOUS *DEFEAT*, OR PART OF....

"THE STING"-- BATMAN STYLE

MIKE W. BARR, WRITER
DON NEWTON &
DENNIS JENSEN, ARTISTS
TODD KLEIN, LETTERER
ADRIENNE ROY, COLORIST
LEN WEIN, EDITOR

IT TRAVERSES THE GOTHAM CITY STREETS, FILLING THE CRISP AFTERNOON AIR WITH *SOUND*...

KEEP OUR KIDS OFF THE STREETS-- AND OUT OF TROUBLE! GIVE TO THE *GOTHAM BOYS' LEAGUE!*

HELP ROBIN FIGHT JUVENILE DELINQUENCY GIVE TO THE GOTHAM BOYS' LEAGUE

DONATIONS

BUT SOON THE LOUDSPEAKER *STOPS* --TO BE REPLACED BY THE DRY RUSTLE OF *BILLS*...

NO NEED TO *SHOVE*, FOLKS ...WE'LL BE GLAD TO *TAKE* AS MUCH AS YOU WANT TO *GIVE!*

I'VE NEVER HEARD OF 'EM *EITHER* --BUT IF *ROBIN'S* ENDORSING THEM, THEY'RE *LEGIT!*

AND SEVERAL THOUSAND DONATIONS LATER...

WOW! MR. SINCLAIR, THIS MUST'VE BEEN OUR BEST DAY THIS WEEK! WHAT'S THE *TOTAL*, MR. BURNS?

NOW, SON, I TOLD YOU TO CALL ME *BRONCO* -- *BRONCO BURNS!* BUT WE'RE ROLLIN' IN *DOUGH!*

IF I INTERPRET MY ASSOCIATE'S COLORFUL JARGON *CORRECTLY*, ROBIN ...

...WE'VE MORE THAN MADE OUR QUOTA FOR THE WEEK! FIFTY THOUSAND DOLLARS!

BAGGING CROOKS WITH BRUCE IS *GREAT*, BUT THIS GIVES ME A CHANCE TO *HELP* KIDS...

...AND I'D RATHER SEE 'EM PUNCHING *BAGS* THAN *COPS*, ANY DAY...!

PRETTY WEAK PUN... LACKS *PUNCH*...!

≈Yawn≈ I *AM* TIRED...

...FOR THE NEXT MORNING WILL BRING NIGHTMARES ENOUGH!

--POLICE REPORT NO LEADS IN THE 50,000 DOLLAR ROBBERY OF *GOTHAM BOYS' LEAGUE* HEAD- QUARTERS, BROKEN INTO OVERNIGHT!

WHAT TH--?!

CALM *DOWN*, DICK...

TERRIFIC! CATCH YOU *NEXT WEEK!*

FOR EIGHT HOURS, DICK GRAYSON SLEEPS THE SLEEP OF THE BONE-WEARY. HE DOES NOT *DREAM*, WHICH IS FORTUNATE...

...I'VE READ THE EARLY POLICE REPORTS, AND SOMETHING DEFINITELY **SMELLS!** YOU'LL NEED **THE BATMAN'S** HELP ON THIS ONE!

AW, COME **ON**, BRUCE... NO NEED FOR **BOTH** OF US TO SOLVE A SIMPLE **ROBBERY!**

KLIK

ROBIN **RAISED** THOSE FUNDS, AND ROBIN SHOULD **RECOVER** THEM-- **SOLO!** I-- **HUH?!**

THOSE PHOTOS... **MUG SHOTS** OF SINCLAIR AND BURNS! BRUCE, WHAT'S GOING **ON?**

HAVE A **SEAT**, DICK-- THIS IS GOING TO **HURT!**

SINCLAIR AND BURNS HAVE POLICE RECORDS OLDER THAN **YOU** ARE! THEY'RE **CON MEN**, DICK!

THEY CLAIM THE MONEY WAS **STOLEN**, AND NO ONE CAN PROVE **OTHERWISE!**

I...I NEVER EVEN RAN A **CHECK** ON THEM...I REALLY BLEW IT THIS TIME...

CHALK IT UP TO **EXPERIENCE**, SON... BUT DON'T WORRY-- I HAVE A PLAN TO STING THOSE TWO CON-ARTISTS **BACK!**

I **APPRECIATE** THAT, BRUCE, BUT I **MESSED UP** ON MY OWN--

--AND I'LL GET THAT MONEY BACK... **ON MY OWN!**

HAVE IT YOUR WAY! GOOD LUCK, CHUM!

ROBIN **MEANS** WELL, BUT HE'S IN OVER HIS HEAD THIS TIME...

WHETHER HE LIKES IT OR NOT, HE'S GOING TO **GET** SOME HELP-- IF NOT FROM **THE BATMAN**...

...THEN FROM **SOMEONE ELSE!**

TAKE A **LOAD** OFF YER FEET, MALONE -- BUT CAREFUL WITH THE **MATCHES**! WE ALREADY HAD **ONE** SET-TO WITH THE SPRINKLERS T'DAY!

I C'N **SEE** THAT!

WHAT DO YOU **WANT** WITH **US**, MALONE? YOU'RE A **GANGSTER**! MY ASSOCIATE AND I ARE--

CON MEN, SINCLAIR-- FIRST CLASS! THAT SCAM YOU PULLED ON ROBIN WAS A-1 **PRIME**!

"SCAM"? MY DEAR SIR, WE WERE **ROBBED**--

THE **COPS** MAY BUY THAT, SINCLAIR-- **I** KNOW BETTER!

THIS IS WHAT'CHA CALL A **BEARER'S BOND**! MATURES IN SIX MONTHS TO BE WORTH A **GRAND** TO THE OWNER! I LIFTED A **HUNDRED** OF 'EM FROM **WAYNE ENTERPRISES**!

WHY IN TARNATION TELL **US**, MR. MALONE?

CALL ME **MATCHES**, BRONCO -- WE'RE GONNA BE **PARTNERS**!

I GOT A HUNDRED GRAND WORTH'A **BONDS**, -- BUT NOT FOR **SIX MONTHS**! I NEED FIFTY GRAND, **CASH**, BY TOMORROW!

WE **TRADE** -- CASH FOR BONDS-- AND YOU INCREASE YOUR INVESTMENT **ONE HUNDRED PERCENT**. WHADDAYA SAY?

THE EYES OF THE CON MEN MEET -- AND AN INSTANT **LATER**...

WE **ACCEPT** YOUR PROPOSITION, MR.--UH--MATCHES! SHALL WE SAY... **MIDNIGHT**... AT THE ALLEY OFF SPICER STREET?

DEAL! PLEASURE DOIN' BUSINESS WITH YA...

SNAP

...**SUCKERS**! THE **AMATEURS** NEVER QUIT WHILE THEY'RE AHEAD!

NOW IF I CAN JUST KEEP **DICK** FROM CATCHING ON...!

AND THAT EVENING...

YOU'LL HAVE TO TAKE THE EVENING PATROL, CHUM! I'VE GOT **JLA SATELLITE DUTY**!

SURE, BRUCE! **NO** SWEAT!

GREAT! HE'LL BE OUT OF MY **WAY**!

29

AND AS THE FULL MOON RISES, WHILE ONE AVENGER OF EVIL PREPARES A *DECEPTION...*

...SO DOES *ANOTHER...!*

THIS INFLATABLE BODY-STOCKING *ALMOST* GIVES ME BRUCE'S BUILD...HIS COSTUME IS STILL A LITTLE *BIG* ON ME...

...BUT IN THE *NIGHT,* IF I HOLD THE *CAPE* AROUND ME...

...IT JUST MIGHT *WORK!*

MINUTES LATER, TWO AVENGERS OF EVIL DEPART, EACH IN SEARCH OF PREY...

...BUT ONE FINDS THE HUNTING GROUND HAS BEEN *RELOCATED!*

I GOT HERE JUST IN TIME-- WONDER WHERE THEY'RE *GOING?*

MOMENTS LATER...

WHOEVER THEY'RE MEETING, THEY BROUGHT THE MONEY *WITH* 'EM! THAT'LL MAKE MY JOB EASIER...

...MAYBE A ROBIN CAN BAG *TWO* BIRDS WITH *ONE* STONE!

THANK YOU, MR.--*er*--MATCHES! IT IS INDEED A *PLEASURE* DOING--

L-LOOK!

BRONCO! WHAT'S THE *MATTER?!*

GAPE IN *AWE,* SPAWN OF EVIL--

30

THE BATMAN IS HERE ... TO PUNISH YOU FOR YOUR WRONGDOING! RETURN THE MONEY YOU STOLE--OR TASTE MY VENGEANCE!

BLAST!

EVEN DISGUISED, I'D KNOW ROBIN'S VOICE ANYWHERE! I ADMIRE THE KID'S SPUNK...

... BUT HE MAY BLOW THE WHOLE DEAL ...

...AND GET HIMSELF KILLED IN THE PROCESS! BURNS' FILE SAID HE WAS TRIGGER-HAPPY!

ONLY ONE CHOICE ...!

NO NEED FER HARDWARE-- I'LL TAKE CARE'A OL' POINTY-EARS MYSELF!

HUH? BA--MALONE! WHAT ARE YOU--

...AS I SUSPECTED-- ROBIN'S BODY STOCKING HAMPERS HIS MOVEMENT ENOUGH TO GIVE ME AN EASY EDGE--

--AS WELL AS CUSHIONING MY PUNCHES! ROBIN WILL JUST GET THE WIND KNOCKED OUT OF HIM!

--UHHHH!

WHEE-OH! YUH SURE HOGTIED HIM, MATCHES!

INDEED! IT APPEARS THE BATMAN'S REPUTATION HAS BEEN HIGHLY...ENHANCED! SHALL WE END IT... PERMANENTLY?

WHUF!

NAH! OFF HIM, AND YA GOT A MILLION OTHER SUPER-DUDES AFTER YA!

JUST SCRAM! I'LL KEEP BATS OUTTA YER HAIR!

SNAP!

THANK YOU, MR. MALONE--FOR EVERYTHING!

31

OOOH... ANYBODY GET THE LICENSE NUMBER OF THAT...*TRUCK*?

SORRY TO ROUGH YOU UP, ROBIN -- BUT THOSE CON MEN WOULD HAVE DONE A LOT *WORSE*!

I *UNDERSTAND*, BATMAN... I JUST WISH I'D DONE *SOMETHING* RIGHT ON THIS CASE! I HAD NO IDEA I'D BE STEPPING ON YOUR *SET-UP*!

FFSSS

EXACTLY, ROBIN -- YOU PREPARED YOUR *OWN* PLAN, WITHOUT ANY HELP FROM ME... A *GOOD* PLAN, TOO!

JUST DO ME ONE *FAVOR* NEXT TIME, CHUM?

WHAT'S *THAT*?

NEXT TIME, DON'T WRITE YOUR OWN *DIALOGUE*! YOUR "*BATMAN*" IS *ABOMINABLE*!

HAHAHAHAHA!

SEVERAL HUNDRED MILES FROM GOTHAM CITY... AND SEVERAL HOURS *LATER*...

--THIS JUST IN: GOTHAM CITY POLICE HAVE RECOVERED THE $50,000 STOLEN FROM THE *GOTHAM BOYS' LEAGUE*!

CONSARN! THE BATMAN MUSTA *STUNG* MALONE AFTER ALL! BUT AT LEAST *WE* STILL GOT--

NO! OH, *NO*!

THESE *BONDS*-- NOTHING BUT *BAT-SHAPES*! THEY'RE *WORTHLESS*!

THE BATMAN STUNG *US*, TOO! BUT HOW? *HOW*?

I DUNNO ABOUT *YEW*, PARTNER...

...BUT I AIN'T NEVER GOIN' *BACK* T'FIND *OUT*! AH'M GIVIN' GOTHAM CITY A *WIDE BERTH* FROM NOW ON!

AGREED, MR. BURNS. =SIGH= ...*AGREED*!

-END-

THE MANY LIVES OF ROBIN

Two of the tales in this annual feature the Batman battling alongside Robin, the boy wonder. You may have been confused, though, by the fact that these two brightly garbed crimefighters appear to be two different people. In "The Sting: Batman Style" Robin is in his late teens and otherwise known as Dick Grayson. Yet in "Fear For Sale" Robin seems to be a few years younger, and is referred to as Jason. What's it all about? Read on...

Robin originally joined the Batman a year or so after the Gotham Guardian donned his dark mantle for the first time. The Batman was present when young Dick Grayson, boy trapeze artist and all round daredevil, watched his beloved parents murdered by agents of gangster Boss Zucco. Years before, young Bruce Wayne had similarly seen his parents cut down in the street by the bullets of one Joe Chill, this single incident providing the impetus for Bruce's crimefighting career. The Batman, therefore, knew something of how Dick felt at that tragic moment. He offered Dick a way to channel his anger, a way to bring Boss Zucco and men like him to justice. He took Dick under his wing and trained him in detective skills and fighting arts, making him more than a talented acrobat, making him... Robin, the boy wonder.

ENTER ROBIN (I)

Clad in bright red, green and yellow, and named after the legendary Robin Hood, Dick was able to end the threat of Boss Zucco for good. The purpose for which Robin had been created was fulfilled, but Dick chose to stay at the Batman's side, as ward to Bruce Wayne and partner to his alter ego. Dick came to terms with the death of his parents, and in time became the cheerful hero known to millions, his brash manner and youth causing many a felon to underestimate him.

Time passed and Dick left Gotham City for New York's Hudson University, majoring in Business and Law. He became full time leader of the Teen Titans, a group of young heroes who – for the most part – had followed in Robin's wake as kid partners to adult crimefighters. He is still with them today, having taken a new name and costume as a mark of his adulthood and independence of the Batman. Despite occasional differences, though, Dick still visits Gotham from time to time, aiding the Batman where necessary.

Despite Dick's activities as Nightwing, the Batman and Robin team continued to protect Gotham. For, after Dick's departure, Batman took on a new sidekick, Jason Todd. Jason was a street kid, forced to fend for himself following the death of his mother and the jailing of his father, a henchman of the evil Two Face. The Batman first encountered Jason when he returned from a spot of crime-busting to find someone had stolen the wheels from the Bat-mobile! Guess who? Jason wasn't bad, just bored and misguided.

The woman mainly responsible for this misdirection was one Fay Gunn, 'head' of a 'school' for underprivileged kids – she took them in off the streets, trained them for crime, and threw them right back. Jason helped the Batman wreck the racket and – impressed by his bravery, brightness and brashness – decided the time was right for a new Robin. Also, he believed that left to his own devices Jason would drift towards crime again and misuse his gifts.

ENTER ROBIN (II)

After a crash course in Basic Robin Skills Jason took to the streets at the Batman's side. Unlike Dick, though, he showed a disturbing tendency to ignore the Batman's orders and advice forged from years of experience fighting in the dark of Gotham's streets. Jason also lacked the self-discipline it took to replace Dick, and would neglect his schoolwork to sneak off looking for criminals to catch. Partly, this was due to the desperate need he felt to prove to the Batman that he was worthy of the Robin costume and name – Dick was a tough act to follow and the Batman was apt to mention this fact perhaps too often. The Batman may have been a brilliant crimefighter, but he wasn't always the most sensitive of substitute fathers. He took Jason off active duty, feeling he needed more time to come to terms with the death of his parents.

EXIT ROBIN

Shortly thereafter, Jason learned that the woman he thought his natural mother had been his father's **second** wife. His birth mother was still alive, working and living in Africa. Assuming the Batman would try to put him off, Jason took off on his own and did eventually locate her. Unfortunately, rather than being the loving figure he expected, Jason's mom turned out to be in cahoots with the villainous **Joker.** She betrayed Jason into his hands and, having savagely beaten Jason, the ever-grateful Clown Prince of Crime locked them **both** in an abandoned building – together with a time bomb. Before the Batman – having followed Jason from America – could reach them and defuse the bomb, mother and son met their maker. Robin the boy wonder was dead.

The Batman took full responsibility for Jason's early death and swore never again to take a young partner into battle with him. Driven by his feelings of loss and guilt the Batman became even more obsessed with cleaning up Gotham than previously. He became darker, more violent. Where previously he had used minimum force when dealing with 'criminal scum' he now lashed out with everything he had, putting crook after crook in hospital with serious injuries. More, he no longer carefully planned his attacks on crime, preferring to "think" with his fists and blocking out the pain of Jason's death. This allowed many a felon he would previously have taken out with one arm, blindfolded, being able to do him fairly serious injury. The occasional torn ligaments and bruises of previous times gave way to wounds from shotguns, knives and more, injuries which belied the Batman's long experience of crimefighting. Alfred, the Batman's faithful manservant, began to spend most of his time doctoring his master's wounds. And the Batman ignored Alfred's advice to take it easy, slow down, re-think his objective and methods and become the capable Batman of old.

ENTREAT ROBIN

Someone who shared Alfred's views was teenager Tim Drake.

Young Tim had been present at Haly's Circus on the night Dick Grayson's parents were murdered. He had his photograph taken with the Flying Graysons and was impressed at the skills of Dick, not much older than him. Tim watched, horrified, as Dick's parents fell to their deaths, and saw Dick leave afterwards with the Batman. Some months later, Robin appeared for the first time and, learning that Dick had become ward of Bruce Wayne, Tim concluded that Bruce and Dick were Batman and Robin. Tim continued to follow the career of Batman and Robin, noting that when Dick moved to New York and Robin publicly became Nightwing the Batman fought crime alone. Then, Bruce Wayne adopted Jason Todd and suddenly there was a new Robin. The death of the second Robin never became public knowledge but Jason's death was reported – though the actual circumstances were not detailed. The Batman was alone once more and, like Alfred, Tim was worried by the deterioration of the Batman's crimefighting techniques and lack of concern for the safety of self and others. So far as Tim was concerned the Batman **needed** a Robin.

ENTOMB ROBIN

Tim confronted Dick with this information, and tried to convince him to forego his Nightwing identity and return to the Batman's side as Robin. Dick refused, but did agree to help the Batman in his current case against Two Face, leaving Tim and Alfred to mind the Batcave. He found the Batman, who agreed to

accept Nightwing's help on the case, but the two wound up in the rubble of a building exploded by the villain.

When the former Dynamic Duo failed to return, Tim realised something must have gone badly wrong, and reluctantly donned the Robin costume himself. Using his intelligence and athletic skills Tim rescued the Batman and Nightwing, and helped them bring in Two Face. The obvious thing was for Tim to take up the mantle of Robin permanently, but despite the enthusiasm of Dick and Alfred for this, the Batman decided against it. He did, though, agree to train Tim in crimefighting techniques so that one day he **might** become a new Robin.

ENTER ROBIN (III)

Tim's parents, international business people who had placed him in a Gotham boarding school to give him an education and stable life, crossed a villain named the Obeah Man. This voodoo ganglord took them captive in Haiti and held them to ransom. Following standing orders from the Drakes, their right hand man refused and – despite the efforts of the Batman – Tim's mother died and his father was left comatose, perhaps for life. Like Bruce and Dick, Tim had now suffered a tragic loss. The Batman tried to help by taking legal responsibility for Tim as he had for Dick and Jason. Soon afterwards the Scarecrow (who can be seen battling the Batman and Jason/Robin in this very annual) came to town and the Batman took him on. The Pharaoh of Phobias got the better of him, leaving it to Tim to bail him out, disguised by a ski mask. Tim saved the day, and both he and the Batman agree he had earned the right to the Robin name, to fight crime at the side of the Batman. Tim was reluctant to don the costume worn by Jason and Dick, though, despite the blessing of the latter. Understanding this, the Batman had created for Tim a redesigned costume, reminiscent of the previous Robin garb but sufficiently different to make it Tim's own. Tim was free to create his own chapter in the history of Robin, liberated from the shadow of Dick and the spectre of Jason.

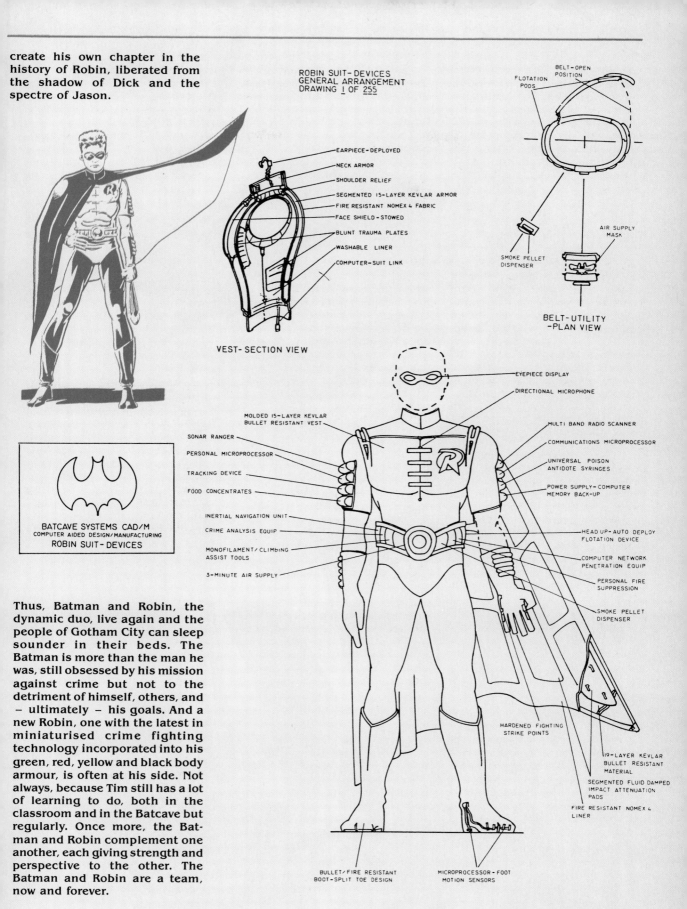

ROBIN SUIT- DEVICES
GENERAL ARRANGEMENT
DRAWING 1 OF 255

EARPIECE-DEPLOYED
NECK ARMOR
SHOULDER RELIEF
SEGMENTED 15-LAYER KEVLAR ARMOR
FIRE RESISTANT NOMEX 4 FABRIC
FACE SHIELD - STOWED
BLUNT TRAUMA PLATES
WASHABLE LINER
COMPUTER-SUIT LINK

VEST- SECTION VIEW

BELT-OPEN POSITION
FLOTATION PODS

SMOKE PELLET DISPENSER

AIR SUPPLY MASK

BELT-UTILITY -PLAN VIEW

EYEPIECE DISPLAY
DIRECTIONAL MICROPHONE

MOLDED 15-LAYER KEVLAR BULLET RESISTANT VEST
SONAR RANGER
PERSONAL MICROPROCESSOR
TRACKING DEVICE
FOOD CONCENTRATES

INERTIAL NAVIGATION UNIT
CRIME ANALYSIS EQUIP
MONOFILAMENT/ CLIMBING ASSIST TOOLS
3-MINUTE AIR SUPPLY

MULTI BAND RADIO SCANNER
COMMUNICATIONS MICROPROCESSOR
UNIVERSAL POISON ANTIDOTE SYRINGES
POWER SUPPLY-COMPUTER MEMORY BACK-UP

HEAD UP- AUTO DEPLOY FLOTATION DEVICE
COMPUTER NETWORK PENETRATION EQUIP
PERSONAL FIRE SUPPRESSION
SMOKE PELLET DISPENSER

HARDENED FIGHTING STRIKE POINTS

19-LAYER KEVLAR BULLET RESISTANT MATERIAL
SEGMENTED FLUID DAMPED IMPACT ATTENUATION PADS
FIRE RESISTANT NOMEX 4 LINER

BULLET/FIRE RESISTANT BOOT-SPLIT TOE DESIGN

MICROPROCESSOR- FOOT MOTION SENSORS

BATCAVE SYSTEMS CAD/M
COMPUTER AIDED DESIGN/MANUFACTURING
ROBIN SUIT- DEVICES

Thus, Batman and Robin, the dynamic duo, live again and the people of Gotham City can sleep sounder in their beds. The Batman is more than the man he was, still obsessed by his mission against crime but not to the detriment of himself, others, and – ultimately – his goals. And a new Robin, one with the latest in miniaturised crime fighting technology incorporated into his green, red, yellow and black body armour, is often at his side. Not always, because Tim still has a lot of learning to do, both in the classroom and in the Batcave but regularly. Once more, the Batman and Robin complement one another, each giving strength and perspective to the other. The Batman and Robin are a team, now and forever.

SMELL THE BURNING RUBBER? HEAR THOSE SCREECHING TIRES? SEE THOSE CARS STREAK AROUND THE TRACK? THIS COULD BE ONLY ONE PLACE...

...A RACETRACK! WOW, THIS IS GREAT, BRUCE!

REMEMBER, WE'RE HERE ON BUSINESS, JAY...

...TWO MAJOR SPORTS FIGURES HAVE BEEN INVOLVED IN SUSPICIOUS-LOOKING ACCIDENTS IN THE PAST WEEK.

A PROMINENT HIGH-DIVER NEARLY BROKE HIS BACK, TRYING A QUINTUPLE SOMERSAULT--WHICH NO ONE HAS EVER SUCCESSFULLY PERFORMED...

...AND AN AWARD-WINNING HANG-GLIDER ALMOST LOST HIS LIFE WHEN HE SWOOPED TOO LOW TO THE GROUND TO RECOVER.

THOSE ATHLETES WERE TOO GOOD TO TAKE CHANCES LIKE THAT-- AND I'M TOO SUSPICIOUS TO WRITE IT OFF AS COINCIDENCE.

...AND INTRO-DUCING THE MAN YOU ALL CAME HERE TO SEE...

JACK HOGAN, THREE-TIME WINNER OF THE *INDIANAPOLIS 500!*

ANNNND THEY'RE *OFF!*

RROARRRR

KROOM

SEE ANY-THING, BRUCE?

NOTHING *YET,* BUT-- *WAIT!*

HOGAN'S NOT WEARING HIS *SAFETY* HARNESS --AND THAT *LOOK* ON HIS FACE... AS THOUGH HE'S GAMBLING WITH HIS *LIFE,* AND DOESN'T *CARE...*

COME *ON,* JAY, I'VE GOT A *HUNCH!* I HOPE I'M *WRONG* ABOUT THIS...

...BUT UN-FORTUNATELY, I RARELY *AM!*

...AND THEY APPROACH THE *HAIRPIN TURN* WITH HOGAN IN SECOND POSITION --HE'S *GOT* TO PULL BACK...

39

...BUT **NO,** HE'S **POURING IT ON!** TWO CARS CAN'T TAKE THAT TURN AT THE SAME TIME! SOMETHING'S GOT TO--

HE WON'T LAST A **MINUTE** IN THERE!

YOU CAN'T GO **AFTER** HIM, BATMAN! YOU'D BE BURNED **ALIVE!**

NOT IF YOU KEEP **HOSING ME DOWN!**

I--I DON'T KNOW IF I CAN **DO** IT, BATMAN...

KEEP THAT SPRAY ON HIM... THAT'S RIGHT...

IS HE *OKAY*?

I DON'T *KNOW* -- BUT HE'D BE DEAD FOR SURE, IF NOT FOR *YOU*.

MEDIC!

MEDIC!

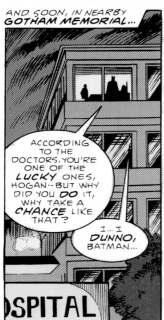

AND SOON, IN NEARBY *GOTHAM MEMORIAL*...

ACCORDING TO THE DOCTORS, YOU'RE ONE OF THE *LUCKY* ONES, HOGAN-- BUT WHY DID YOU *DO* IT, WHY TAKE A *CHANCE* LIKE THAT?

I... I *DUNNO*, BATMAN...

OSPITAL

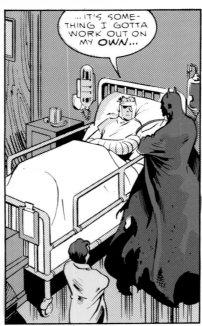

...IT'S SOME- THING I GOTTA WORK OUT ON MY *OWN*...

...BUT I'D DO IT AGAIN, IN A *MINUTE*!

THERE'S SOME- THING HOGAN ISN'T *TELLING* US, JAY, BUT THIS *BLOOD SAMPLE* I TOOK FROM THE HOSPITAL *LAB* MAY SPEAK *FOR* HIM...

... I THINK I DETECT A PSYCHO-ACTIVE CHEMICAL I'VE ENCOUNTERED *BEFORE*...

... BUT ONCE I'VE COMPARED IT TO OUR *FILE* SLIDE...

... I'LL KNOW FOR *SURE*.

HOISAN'S BLOOD — FILE COPY SC 7743

S 3000

I WAS *RIGHT*...

...THIS IS A CHEMICAL USED EXCLUSIVELY BY THE *SCARECROW*. BACKGROUND ON HIM, JAY?

Uh... LET'S SEE... REAL NAME'S *CRAIG*... NO, *CRANE*... JONATHAN CRANE...

"...HE WAS A *PSYCHOLOGY PROFESSOR*... TALENTED, BUT DIDN'T HAVE A LOTTA *FRIENDS*..."

THERE'S THAT FUNNY PROFESSOR *CRANE* AGAIN...

...HE'S SO *FUNNY-LOOKING*... LIKE A *SCARECROW*...

THEY LAUGH AT ME BECAUSE I'D RATHER SPEND MONEY ON *BOOKS* THAN ON FANCY *CLOTHES*, OR STUPID *PARTIES*...

...BUT IF I COULD USE MY *BOOKS* TO *GET* MONEY... *THEN* THEY WOULDN'T LAUGH AT ME... THEY'D *FEAR* ME...

THE PSYCHOLOGY OF FEAR

43

"...AND CRANE'S BEEN AT IT EVER *SINCE.* BUT I FEEL KINDA *SORRY* FOR HIM, BRUCE..."

"...I MEAN, NOBODY LIKES TO BE *LAUGHED* AT...

I *KNOW,* JAY--BUT I CAN'T ALLOW HIM TO TAKE HIS *HUMILIATION* OUT ON *SOCIETY.*

YOUR NEW COSTUME, MASTER BRUCE... I'M AFRAID THE OLD ONE WAS PAST SAVING.

FORTUNES OF *WAR,* ALFRED.

I *HOPE,* WHEN THIS NIGHT IS OVER...

...A UNIFORM IS *ALL* WE'VE LOST.

"IT MIGHT BE A *LONG* NIGHT ALFRED--DON'T *WAIT UP.*"

...BUT BATMAN FIGURES THE SCARECROW MIGHT TRY SOMETHING *TONIGHT,* SO I MONITOR THE *BUG* HE PLANTED IN HOGAN'S ROOM, AND--

BORRRRING. WAITING FOR THE BAD GUY TO SHOW UP IS DULLER'N WATCHING *PAINT DRY.*

UH oh....!

AND HOW ARE WE FEELING TONIGHT, MR. HOGAN?

NOT *BAD,* DOC...BUT I WANT *OUTTA* HERE, SO I CAN *RACE* AGAIN!

THAT'S *GOOD,* HOGAN...YOU'RE DOING EXACTLY AS I *PLANNED!*

YOU AIN'T NO DOCTOR--!

BRILLIANT *DIAGNOSIS,* HOGAN...

...A MINOR ATTACK OF *PATHOPHOBIA* --FEAR OF *DISEASE* --SCATTERED THE DEAR AND GLORI-OUS *PHYSICIANS,* LEAVING US *ALONE!*

YOU! YOU GOT ME *INTA* THIS MESS... YOU GOTTA GET ME *OUT!*

YES, YES, I MADE YOU TAKE MY NEW DRUG...THE ONE WHICH *REMOVES* FEAR FROM THE BRAIN.

YOU DIDN'T *TELL* ME IT'D MAKE ME TAKE *CHANCES* --TAKE AWAY MY *COMMON* SENSE...!

BUT WHAT, AFTER ALL, *IS* COMMON SENSE BUT A FORM OF *FEAR...?* NOW YOU'LL PAY *DEARLY* FOR THE *ANTIDOTE,* HOGAN, $50,000, OR--*EH?*

KRAASH

IT'S *ME,* BAGGY-PANTS...

45

46

47

... I WIN AGAIN.

HEEEHOHAHOHEEHAAA

NOT LONG AFTER, IN A LONELY HOUSE ON THE OUTSKIRTS OF GOTHAM...

...PROFESSIONAL DARE-DEVIL ALVIN KENNER PONDERS HIS NEWEST STUNT...

WIND VELOCITY'S TRICKY UP THERE-- COMPENSATION'S THE IMPORTANT THING...

...AND SPEAKING OF COMPENSATION, MR. KENNER...

WHO --?

WHY SO SURPRISED? I TOLD YOU I'D RETURN, AFTER YOU HAD A CHANCE TO RECONSIDER MY OFFER...

WELL, I HAVE...AND THE ANSWER'S STILL NO. NO HARD FEELINGS, STRAW MAN?

OF COURSE NOT. BUT TELL ME, KENNER...

...DO YOU HAVE A LIGHT?

Uh...SURE. GOT ONE SOMEWHERE AROUND HERE...

CLEVER *DISGUISE*, BATMAN... BUT YOU FAILED MY *TEST*--YOU DIDN'T KNOW THAT KENNER HAS *PYROPHOBIA*--AN OVERWHELMING FEAR OF *FIRE!*

BLAST! EVEN *ROBIN* WOULDN'T MAKE AN ERROR LIKE THAT...

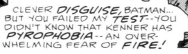

...BUT I *DID!*

MY DRUGGED DART'S ALREADY SLOWING YOU DOWN, BATMAN...

...SO WHY NOT *SHOOT* THE WORKS? HEE HA HO HA *HEEEEE!*

I'M *AFRAID* YOU'RE IN NO CONDITION TO DRIVE, BATMAN--

--SO *THIS* DART...

UNHHHH...

49

SOMETIME LATER...

HE ISN'T HERE YET...

ATLAS CONCRETE

...BUT HE WILL BE! AND THEN--

THEN BATMAN'LL PUT YOU AWAY, YOU STRAW-FILLED CREEP!

WILL HE? I FEAR YOU'RE WRONG, BOY...

...THIS FACTORY IS BOTH FULLY AUTO-MATED AND QUITE THOROUGHLY GUARDED, AS WELL! AND I'VE ADDED A FEW DEVICES OF MY OWN!

SO WHAT? BATMAN'S ESCAPED TRAPS BEFORE!

BUT NOT WHILE UNDER THE INFLUENCE OF MY NEW DRUG! IT RE-MOVES THE NORMAL INHIBITORS--FEARS--FROM THE MIND, MAK-ING MEN CARELESS ...OVERCONFIDENT!

BATMAN WILL FIND HE'S BITTEN OFF MORE THAN HE CAN CHEW...

...AND FIND HE'S EATING HIS LAST MEAL! HEE HA HO HEEEE!

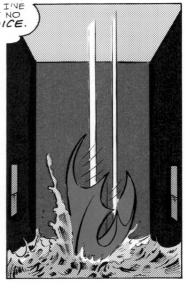

...AND WHEN IT CEASES...

THAT'S THE END OF *HIM!* EITHER HE LEAKS LIKE A *SIEVE,* OR HE *DROWNED* MINUTES AGO!

BATMAN... ≥SOB≤ IT... IT CAN'T BE...

IT'S *NOT.*

BATMAN!

BUT... MY *TRAP...* HOW DID YOU *ESCAPE* --?

ARE YOU *ALL RIGHT,* ROBIN?

ME? WHAT ABOUT *YOU?*

YOU'LL NEVER KNOW.

WHO

I'M FINE -- OR I *WILL* BE, ONCE WE'VE FOUND THE *ANTIDOTE* TO CRANE'S DRUG IN HIS *LABORATORY.* HIS OTHER *VICTIMS* WILL SLEEP EASIER, TOO.

HEY, IT'S OKAY, CHUM.

I... I *KNOW...* I JUST THOUGHT... FOR A *MINUTE* THERE...

HOW *DID* YOU ESCAPE, ANYWAY?

WELL, THE TWO MAIN RISKS WERE BEING *SHOT,* OR *DROWNING...*

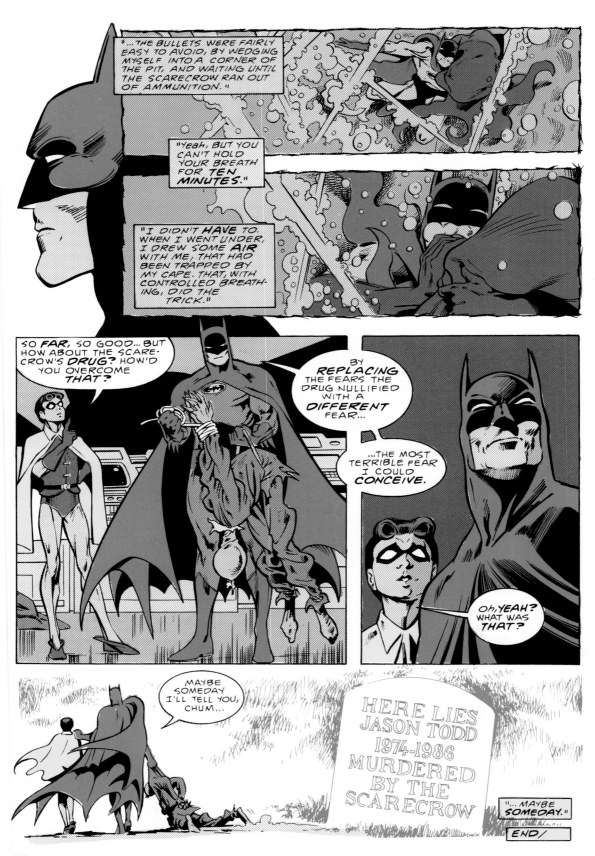

POISON IVY

Alter Ego: Pamela Lillian Isley
Occupation: Adventurer
Known Relatives: Unnamed parents
Group Affiliation: Suicide Squad

Base of Operations: Belle Reve Prison, Louisiana
First Appearance: BATMAN #181 (June, 1966)
Height: 5'6"
Eyes: Green
Weight: 119 lbs.
Hair: Red-brown

HISTORY

Pamela Isley grew up in Seattle, the only child of well-to-do parents who pampered their daughter and indulged her every whim. A cute girl, Pamela was, sadly, emotionally unstable and entirely too critical of her appearance; consequently, she spent most of her adolescence alone and apart from other children. Deciding that if nobody was going to bring her roses she should then just grow her own, Pamela became more and more interested in botany, finding solace in the plants and flowers that always listened to her and depended on her.

Pamela went to college and studied botany under Dr. Jason Woodrue, a brilliant scientist. (Years later, Woodrue would become the plant master known as the Floronic Man, and even later, Floro of the New Guardians.) Woodrue performed his earliest experiments on Pamela, experiments that actually mutated her into a being not quite human, one with an unnatural affinity for and power over plant life. Woodrue eventually left Seattle, but by that time, Pamela had found another love — the Batman, whom she worshipped, idolized, and fantasized about. With her precarious emotional outlook, she became convinced that Batman, too, would fall instantly in love with her should the two of them ever meet face to face. So, using the plant mastery she had gained under Woodrue and adopting the nom de guerre

Poison Ivy, Pamela traveled to Gotham City and began a one-woman crime wave guaranteed to capture the Dark Knight's attention.

The Batman, who generally devotes himself to his war on crime rather than romantic pursuits, spurned Pamela's affections, and she was eventually imprisoned at Arkham Asylum for further psychiatric evaluation. But the power she had tasted as Poison Ivy thrilled Pamela. For the first time in her life, she was able to control others with the power at her command, to manipulate men with her beauty and raw sexuality. Breaking out of Arkham, she decided to continue her criminal career and matched wits with Batman repeatedly, forever being put back behind bars and yet always able to coerce some young, virile guard into looking the other way while she escaped once more.

Eventually, Poison Ivy was broken out of Arkham by Duchess of the Suicide Squad — a task force that allows known supercriminals to negotiate their freedom in exchange for participating in especially dangerous U.S. governmental missions — and recruited into the Squad to help fight the menace of the Loa. Having served her time with the Squad, Ivy fled to the South American country of Puerto Azul, adopted the pseudonym of "Ivita," and set herself up as the power-behind-the-power of military leader General Vaca. She eventually returned to the United States and the Suicide Squad.

As Poison Ivy, Pamela is, first and fore-

most, a manipulator. Her emotions are mercurial, and she is affectionate and trustworthy only to serve her own ends. Her only real vulnerability is her dependence on the power over men that she so loves to wield. She is as cold toward women as she is passionate about men.

POWERS & WEAPONS

Poison Ivy is one of the world's greatest experts in botany. Moreover, as a result of the experiments performed upon her as a college student, she has a number of plant-related paranormal abilities, not the least of which is an ability to use her body chemistry to create certain touch-activated "potions" — truth serums, love potions, and the like.

Poison Ivy's preferred method of "attack" is her *kiss*, which she uses as a conduit for her manipulative power over men. She possesses marginal hand-to-hand combat skills, but does not really need them.

text: MARK WAID/art: KEVIN MAGUIRE & JOE RUBINSTEIN/colors: ANTHONY TOLLIN